....

make believe ideas

The Emperor's New Clothes

Key sound l-blends spellings:
bl, cl, fl, gl, pl, sl
Secondary sounds: k, ld

Written by Rosie Greening
Illustrated by Clare Fennell

Reading with phonics

How to use this book

The **Reading with phonics** series helps you to have fun with your child and to support their learning of phonics and reading. It is aimed at children who have learned the letter sounds and are building confidence in their reading.

Each title in the series focuses on a different key sound or blend of sounds. The entertaining retelling of the story repeats this soun frequently, and the different spellings for the sound or blend of sounds are highlighted in red type. The first activity at the back o the book provides practice in reading and using words containing the sound. This title looks at a key consonant blend group, where two or more consonants are blended together, but each sound may be heard in the blend. The key group of consonant blends for **The Emperor's New Clothes** is the **l-blend**.

Start by reading the story to your child, asking them to join in with the refrain in bold. Next, encourage them to read the story with you. Give them a hand to decode tricky words.

Now look at the activity pages at the back of the book. These are intended for you and your child to enjoy together. Most are not activities to complete in pencil or pen, but by reading and talking or pointing.

The **Key sound** pages focus on one sound or on a group of consonant blends. Encourage your child to read the different letter groups and complete the activity, so they become more aware of the variety of spellings there are for the same sound or for the group of consonant blends.

The **Letters together** pages look at two pairs or groups of letters and at the sounds they make as they work together. Help your child to read the words and trace the route on the word maps.

Rhyme is used a lot in these retellings. Whatever stage your child has reached in their learning of phonics, it is always good practice for them to listen carefully for sounds and find words that rhyme. The pages on **Rhyming words** take six words from the story and ask children to read and find other words that rhyme with them.

The **Key words** pages focus on a number of key words that occur regularly but can nonetheless be challenging. Many of these words are not sounded out following the rules of phonics and the easiest thing is for children to learn them by sight, so that they do not worry about decoding them. These pages encourage children to retell the story, practising key words as they do so.

The **Picture dictionary** page asks children to focus closely on nine words from the story. Encourage children to look carefully at each word, cover it with their hand, write it on a separate piece of paper, and finally, check it!

Do not complete all the activities at once – doing one each time you read will ensure that your child continues to enjoy the stories and the time you are spending together. **Have fun!**

Emperor Claude liked buying suits,

expensive clothes and glitzy boots.

He even had a classy pair

of gleaming, golden underwear!

The emperor held a ball each year,
where he would rudely gloat and jeer.
"My clothes cost more than yours," he'd brag.
"Your cloak looks like a plastic bag!"

Claude shows off without a care.
He's got a lot of clothes to wear.

But one day, Claude was in despair:
"These cloaks are all too bland and bare!
I need new clothes for my next ball.
I am the emperor, after all!"

Some clever robbers stood nearby
and overheard Claude give this cry.
"Let's play a trick," said Flo to Rose,
"and claim that we make special clothes."

Claude thinks all the suits are bare.
Will he find new clothes to wear?

They dressed as tailors right away,
then went to talk to Claude that day.
"For twenty bags of gold," Flo said,
"we'll weave some clothes from glinting thread."

"What kind of clothes?" cried Claude with glee.
Said Rose, "They're clothes that fools can't see.
The floaty fabric's light as air –
it feels like wearing underwear!"

**Claude believes the clever pair.
Will he find new clothes to wear?**

"How glorious!" the emperor said.
"Please get to work – I'm off to bed."
He left them in a pleasant room,
with glistening gold and one, big loom.

But what Claude simply didn't know
was neither thief could even sew!
They played with all their gold instead,
and slept once it was time for bed.

Claude gives them some gold to share.

Will he find new clothes to wear?

Before too long, Claude wished to peek
at all the clothes they'd made that week.
He sent his clever friend called Clare
to check the cloth weaved by the pair.

But when Clare glanced inside the room,
the robbers flew back to the loom.
They flicked their fingers through the air,
pretending cloth was flowing there!

**Clare peeks in and gets a scare.
Will Claude find new clothes to wear?**

Clare looked around in gloom and dread.
She couldn't glimpse a single thread.
"Oh, no!" thought Clare. "What do I do?
If Claude thinks I'm a fool, I'm through!"

So Clare flew back to Emperor Claude
and lied, "The clothes look great, my lord!
The cloak is blue, and very chic.
It's perfect for your ball next week."

Emperor Claude believes young Clare.
Will he find new clothes to wear?

So Claude ran in to see them too.
But there were no clothes in his view!
"If Clare could see the cloth," thought he,
"she's not a fool – it's only me!"

The two sly robbers laughed at Claude.
They asked him, "Are you pleased, my lord?"
The emperor claimed: "I like them all!
I'll be the best-dressed at the ball."

Claude's confused - there's nothing there!
Will he find new clothes to wear?

The day came for Claude's royal ball,
and people flocked into the hall.
They clustered round on tippy-toes
to see the emperor's magic clothes.

Some guessed he'd wear a glittery suit.
Another pictured glitzy boots.
But every guest there knew the rule
and hoped that they were not a fool.

Soon, the guests are everywhere.
Will Claude find new clothes to wear?

When Claude arrived, he struck a pose
to show off all his brand-new clothes.
The guests glanced up, then had to stare:
Claude was in his underwear!

But no one laughed as Claude walked by.

Instead, the guests began to lie!

"What classy cloth! What glitzy thread!

Your clothes are glorious!" they said.

Claude is in his underwear!

Will he find new clothes to wear?

At last, Claude passed a boy called Fred,
who didn't care what others said.
Fred giggled, then he shrieked with glee:
"He's got no clothes on – can't you see?"

The guests all laughed, and Claude blushed rec
"I've been a fool!" the emperor said.

Claude sacked the thieves, and hired Fred to help him choose new clothes instead!

Fred has clothes advice to share.
Claude will buy new clothes to wear!

Key sound

The **l-blends** are **bl**, **cl**, **fl**, **gl**, **pl** and **sl**.
Practise these sounds by looking at the words in the clothes and using them to make sentences.
Can you use each word in a different sentence?

black
blush
blanket
blonde

flag
fly
flute
floor
flower

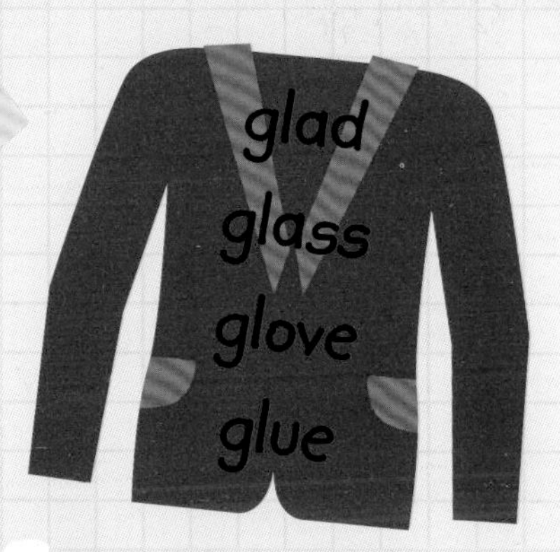

glad
glass
glove
glue

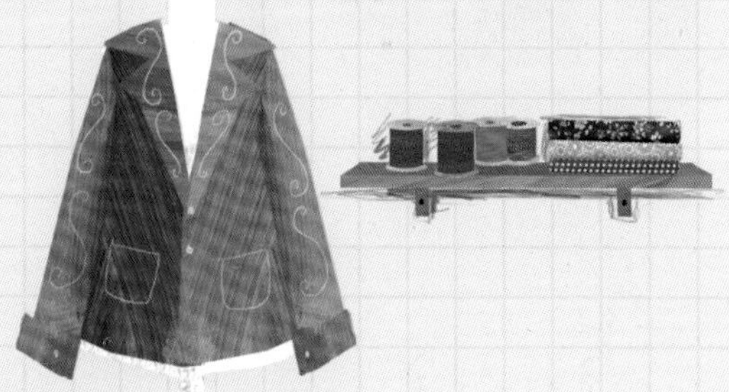

plate
plum
plenty
plane

sleep
slipper
slow
slug

Letters together

Look at these letters and say the sounds they make.

ld

k

Follow the words containing **ld** to pay the robbers in gold.

pose

ld

boy

blue

wild

build

could

dress

gold

Follow the words that contain k to dress the emperor in a cloak.

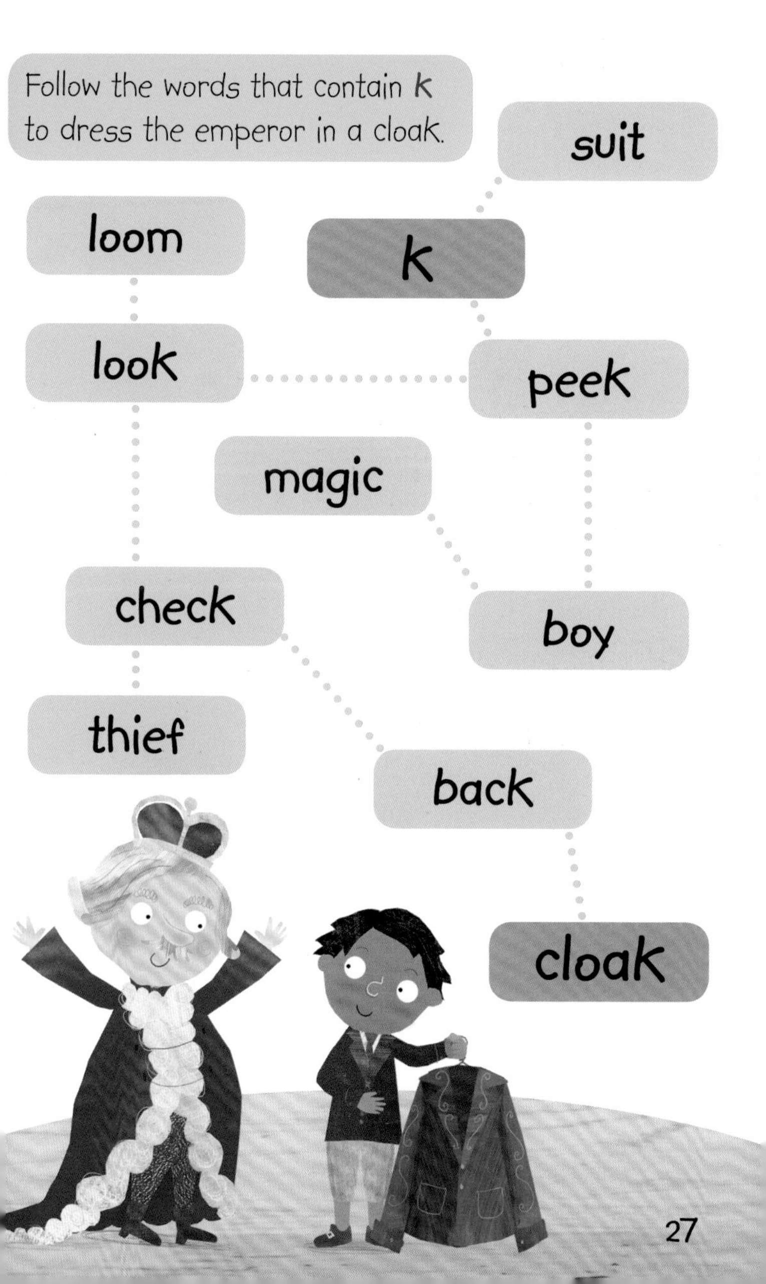

Rhyming words

Read and say the words in the flowers, and then point to other words that rhyme with them.

suit	cloak	spoke
folk		bare

clever	play	say
ball		day

ran	gold	room
cold		told

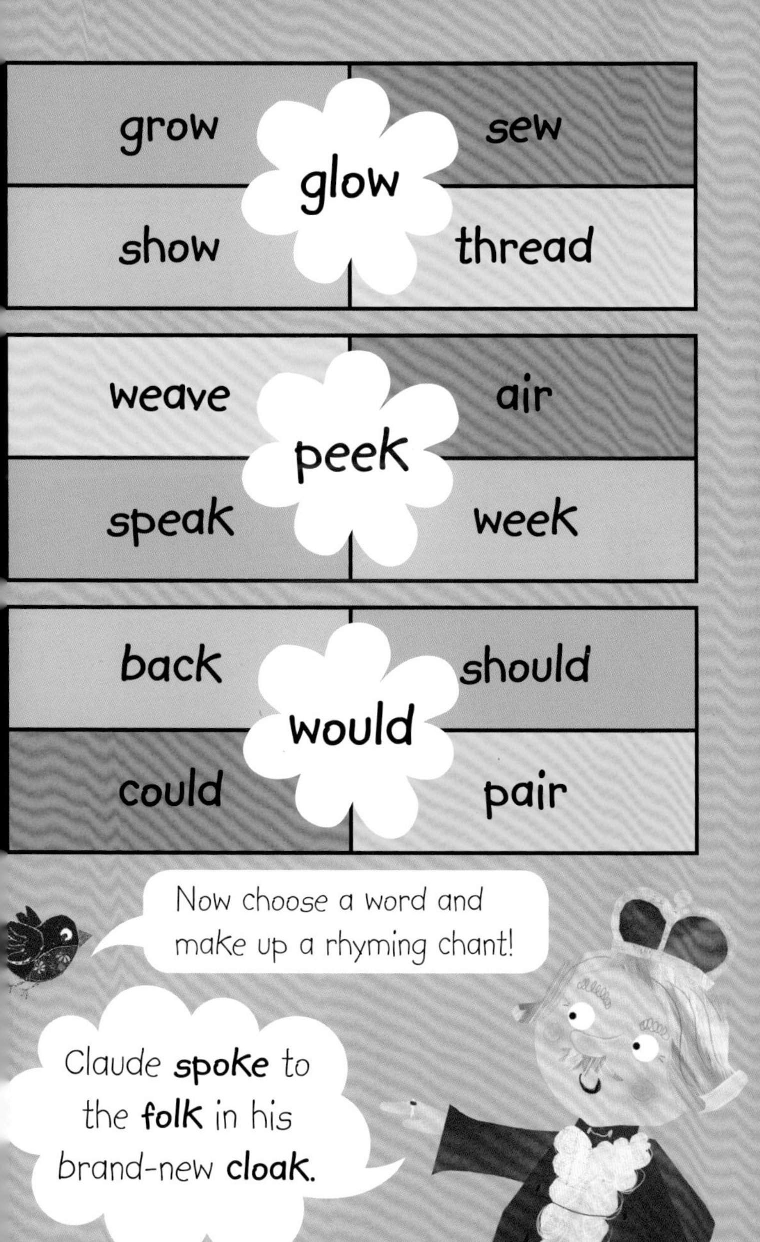
grow
glow
sew
show
thread
weave
peek
air
speak
week
back
would
should
could
pair
Now choose a word and make up a rhyming chant!
Claude **spoke** to the **folk** in his brand-new **cloak**.

Key words

Many common words can be difficult to sound out. Practise them by reading these sentences about the story. Now make more sentences using other key words from around the border.

Emperor Claude **had** lots of clothes.

Two robbers **said** they could make magic clothes.

The robbers pretended to **make** clothes

not • your • asked • his • he

• said • very • a • big • had • made • day • off • on •

Claude said he could **see** the clothes.

The guests turned **up** for the royal ball.

When Claude arrived, he was in his underwear!

eryone lied to Claude except a **little** boy.

The emperor **saw** how foolish he had been.

Claude **asked** the boy for fashion tips.

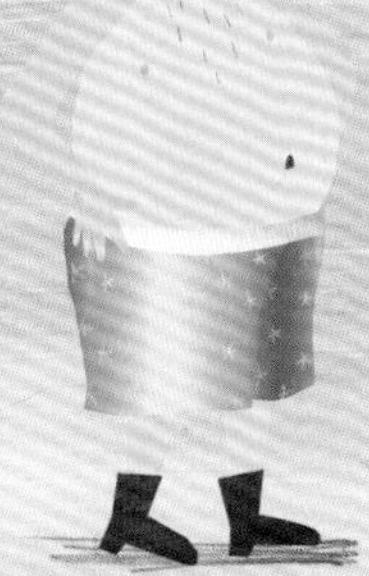

old • see • like • into • there • with • was • to

her • saw • in • when • make • the • called • look • by • about • up • you • they • little

Picture dictionary

Look carefully at the pictures and the words.
Now cover the words, one at a time.
Can you remember how to write them?